# THE OFFICIAL

*Neighbours*™

90

£3·99

Written and edited by Clive Hopwood
with contributions from Marcus Alleyn, Kelly Bourne,
Tim Ewbank, Joe Grizzard, Mike Kidson, Eloise Pratt,
Bridget Steele, Nicole Swengley and Penny Wilgress.

Designed by Ian Gwilt

Picture Credits
Grundy Television 7,8,11,14,21,30,31,46,48,57,58
Australian Tourist Commission 2–3,17,27,41,55,62–63
London Features International Ltd. 12,22,24,25,34,35,
   36,37,38,44,51,
Pictorial Press Limited 6,45,50,52,54
Scope Features 7,15,20,28,56,59
Syndication International (1986) Ltd. 4,18,23,61
Topham Picture Library 5,6,32,42,53

Cover photos supplied by Grundy Television

Published in Great Britain by
World International Publishing Ltd.,
An Egmont Company, Egmont House,
P.O. Box 111, Great Ducie Street,
Manchester M60 3BL
Printed in Italy    ISBN 7235 6859 6
3nd Reprint 1989

# CONTENTS

# G'DAY NEIGHBOURS!

Neighbours may come and neighbours may go but **Neighbours** goes on for ever. With each departing face comes a new arrival — just like in any real street.

And **Neighbours** fans have continued to increase in number, both here in Britain and in other countries. The show is more popular than ever, and still the UK's No.1 soap, no matter what anyone says.

Back in January, Coronation Street, which had been whingeing about EastEnders and **Neighbours** cheating with numbers, did a bit of their own imaginative adding up. The veteran soap began its own omnibus edition on Sunday afternoons.

The world waited with bated breath for the result. They lined up as follows:

| | |
|---|---|
| Coronation Street (Weds/Sun) | 22.97 million |
| Coronation Street (Tues/Sun) | 21.50 |
| EastEnders (Thurs/Sun) | 19.76 |
| Neighbours (Tues) | 19.16 |
| Neighbours (Mon) | 18.81 |
| Neighbours (Thurs) | 18.54 |
| Neighbours (Fri) | 18.50 |
| Neighbours (Weds) | 18.29 |
| EastEnders (Tues/Sun) | 17.62 |

(Come on you poms! There's 3.81 million of you out there who should be trying harder!) "We always knew we were the top soap," said a Coronation Street regular. Top soap when it comes to how many people watch a single, repeated episode. Sure.

But how many people watch per week? Coronation Street 44.47 million. EastEnders 37.38 million. And **Neighbours**? 93.30 million. Now which would you say is the most popular soap? And That's Official!, as they say.

## THE ROBINSONS

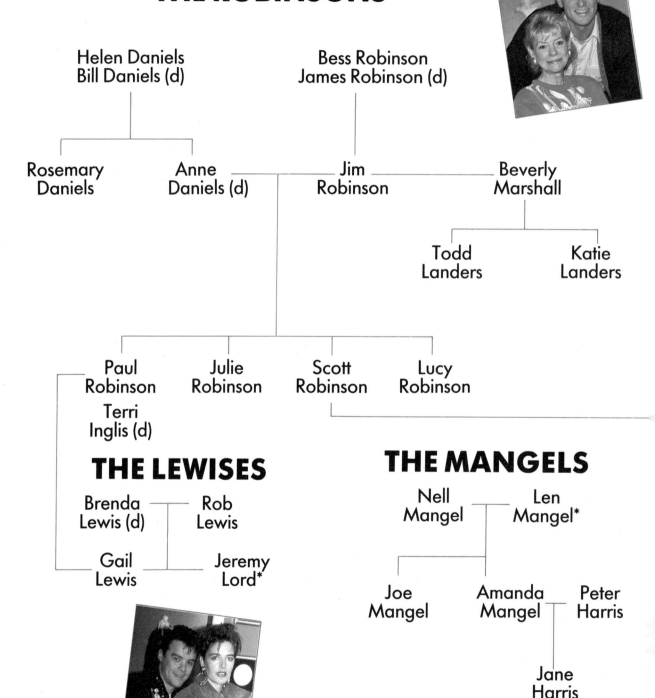

Helen Daniels
Bill Daniels (d)

Bess Robinson
James Robinson (d)

Rosemary
Daniels

Anne
Daniels (d)

Jim
Robinson

Beverly
Marshall

Todd
Landers

Katie
Landers

Paul
Robinson

Terri
Inglis (d)

Julie
Robinson

Scott
Robinson

Lucy
Robinson

## THE LEWISES

Brenda
Lewis (d)

Rob
Lewis

Gail
Lewis

Jeremy
Lord*

## THE MANGELS

Nell
Mangel

Len
Mangel*

Joe
Mangel

Amanda
Mangel

Peter
Harris

Jane
Harris

(d) deceased    * divorced

6

## THE RAMSAYS

Edna Ramsay
Dan Ramsay

Max
Ramsay

Maria
Ramsay

Tom
Ramsay

Doreen
Ramsay (d)

Madge
Ramsay

Fred
Mitchell

Danny
Ramsay

Shane
Ramsay

Henry
Ramsay

Charlene
Mitchell

## THE CLARKES

Eileen
Clarke

Allen
Lawrence

Malcolm
Clarke

Tina
Lawrence

Sally
Wells

Des
Clarke

Daphne
Lawrence (d)

Jamie
Clarke

## THE BISHOPS

Mavis
Bishop (d)

Harold
Bishop

David
Bishop

Kerry
Bishop

Kristian Schmid

# HARD WORK, GOOD FUN

Most 11 and 12-year-olds would gladly give up their weekly pocket money to meet glamorous **Neighbours** stars Craig McLachlan and Annie Jones.

But for Sally Jensen, who plays Kate Landers, and Kristian Schmid (Todd Landers), it doesn't cost a penny — in fact, they get paid for it.

"I love working in **Neighbours**," says an elated Sally, 11. "All the people on the set are great."

"I particularly love Craig and Jason," she adds with a grin. "We're good friends with Craig. He's taught us this really funny handshake."

Now regulars in **Neighbours**, Sally and Kristian, 12, were originally recruited from the Actors' Training Studio shortly after beginning classes.

After five years of nagging her mother, bubbly Sally was enrolled at ATS ... and in just one week she was snapped up by Network Ten producers.

"We went to this audition because the parts popped up," says Sally. "We had one drama lesson and decided to audition for the roles of Kate and Todd. They called us a couple of weeks later and asked, 'Would you like to come in for a screen test?' I always knew I wanted to act, even before I started. I guess I've got a feeling, something inside me that's telling me to do it."

As Kristian has discovered, acting on prime-time television has its rewards. "I've been getting some fan mail, mainly from 13 and 14-year-old girls," says a blushing Kristian. "They ask me how old I am and how long I've been on the show — even where I live."

But Sally has found that success can have its drawbacks. There was a recent holiday, for example, when she found herself surrounded by admirers. That was "a little bit scary," Sally explains. "I went to Fiji for my birthday and quite a lot of people would stare at me. Sometimes it was a bit annoying."

"I want to do something people will remember"

9

# HARD WORK, GOOD FUN

**"I always knew I wanted to act"**

As hopeful and enthusiastic as they are, Sally and Kristian have a firm grip on reality. When they are not on the set, their number one priority is working with Marisa, their tutor, or going to school like other children.

"They're not here full-time," says Marisa, "but it can be four or five days a week. My job is to keep them up to date with their schooling so they don't fall behind and to coach them with their lines."

Kristian and Sally's workload can mean sacrificing time with their family and friends. Kristian, from Geelong, stays with relatives in Melbourne up to four days at a time.

"I think sometimes that it's harder being a kid than an adult," says Kristian. "You can have a scene in the morning and then an hour's break — and then more scenes in the afternoon. When you're working from seven o'clock in the morning to 11 at night, it gets a bit tiring doing school work as well. Instead of having a break to study lines, we have to do school work."

Kristian and Sally want to become professional actors when they grow up — and they know that this requires absolute dedication and commitment. "Since we've started, we've learned how to act properly," says Sally. "But it's been hard work. When someone has to cry, or you have to do something that's really difficult, you have to keep going over the scene again and again."

Even after a gruelling 12-hour day on the set, Ramsay Street's cute twosome are determined to follow their dream. "I think I want to be an actor, but it's not as stable as architecture," says Kristian. "I'd like something to build on. It's not that I want to be noticed — that's not why I want to act. I want to do something that people will remember . . . I don't want to be known as Kristian Schmid, the clothesmaker."

Clearly both Kristian and Sally feel that the hard work involved is worthwhile. "Acting's not that important to some people," says Kristian, "but in the long run, if you're good and work hard, you can help people and really give them something."

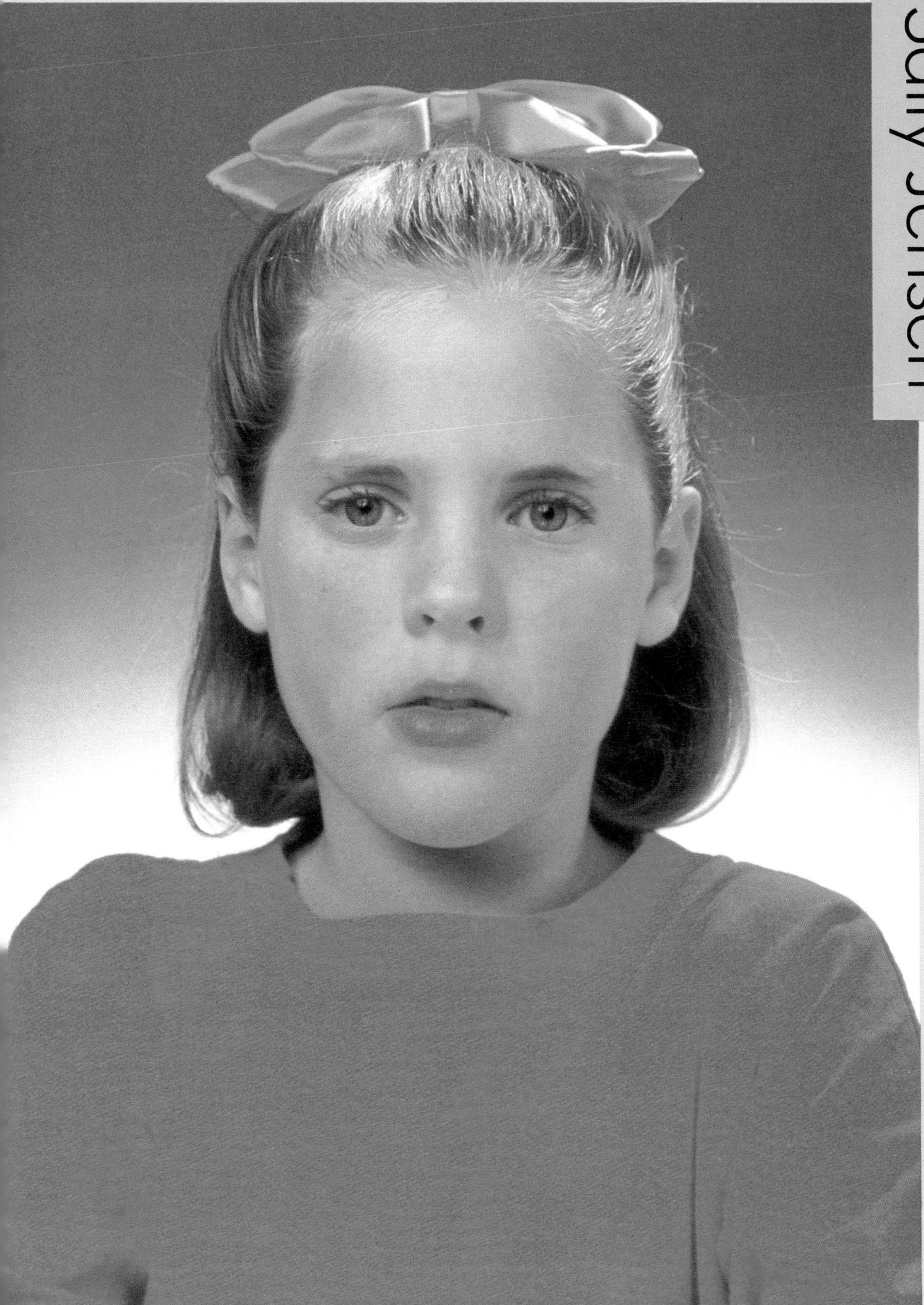

Sally Jensen

# RAMSAY STREET ROMEO

Craig McLachlan

**He's blond, blue-eyed and very, very hunky. But there's also something else that fans of the good-looking hero should know . . . he's very, very married.**

## "I've got lots of plans"

The latest **Neighbours** heart-throb kept his wife, Karen, a medical secretary, hidden because he was worried his marital status would jeopardize his Romeo role. He also wanted to keep Karen out of the glare of publicity. When he did finally own up, he admits his bosses were "a little cool".

Overnight Craig McLachlan became a star. Within days of his first appearance dozens of fans ripped off his T-shirt as he walked through a Sydney shopping centre. "I thought that sort of thing only happened in movies," he says, breaking into his lady-killing grin. "But I've learned to handle these things with a bit of tact and diplomacy . . . secretly I love it!

"There are plenty of elements in Henry that I identify with. He's a fairly zany guy who loves a practical joke, and so do I. He has the same sense of humour as me. And Henry's catch phrase – 'Life isn't meant to be taken seriously' – is something I can sympathize with."

As for his role as the Ramsay Street Romeo, he even jokes that Bouncer, the labrador, is the "only character in the show I haven't tried it on with!"

Playing Charlene's brother, Henry, who's just come out of jail, is particularly poignant because Craig himself admits he was lucky not to have ended up in prison himself.

Craig, 23, a former pop singer and bodybuilder from Shelly Beach, near Sydney, explains: "I sat by my dad's bedside and had to watch a lovely man die a very painful death. I just couldn't understand why. Afterwards I was an unruly rebel. I skipped school and got into some very bad habits, but all that ended when I met my wife, Karen. She really changed my life."

His big break came when he landed roles in two other Aussie soaps, *Sons and Daughters* and *The Young Doctors*. The next step along the road to stardom was **Neighbours** . . .

Now he is watched by an audience of more than 19 million in Britain alone, and is firmly established as a No.1 attraction. But he's still determined to carve out his own niche in the serial and make Henry really popular.

But Craig certainly didn't boost his popularity when he scoffed at how easy he found the gruelling 10-hour daily filming schedule. Even so, Craig has thousands of women fans drooling – for the time being at least. But he won't, he warns, be heart-throb Henry Ramsay for ever. Leaning back contentedly he says, "I've got lots of plans for the future. Films, theatre . . . I want to leave no stone unturned."

## "Life isn't meant to be taken seriously"

# NEIGHBOURS GOSSIP

Indoor shooting for **Neighbours** is done at the Channel 10 Studios at Nunawading, Melbourne.

Holmes and Watson did it! No, not the famous detective and his medical sidekick. This is Ian Holmes, President of Grundy Television, and Reg Watson, the serial's creator, and head of TV Drama with Grundy Television.

Viewers may be forgiven for thinking they may have seen actress Linda Hartley somewhere before. "The first time I was in the show," she explains, "I played one of Paul's early girlfriends. It feels strange being back and playing someone else." Linda's new role as Kerry Bishop, Harold's long-lost daughter, is "a bit of a hippy who has spent the last few years leading an alternative lifestyle wandering around India and Nepal with her baby." That doesn't sound like Paul's cup of tea at all!

The very first words spoken in the first scene of **Neighbours** belonged to Danny Ramsay. Waking from a nightmare he shouted, "Shane! Shane! No! Shane!!! No!!!" He had been dreaming that Shane had been injured in a car crash . . .

Stefan Dennis was born in Tawonga in Victoria state. His wife, Roz Roy, also works in television and is a freelance model. Stefan describes himself as "one of the most energetic people I know!"

Annie Jones' real name is Annika Jasko. Her parents were born in Hungary and emigrated to Australia in the 1950s. Annie's first language is Hungarian — she didn't learn English until she went to school.

Lullaby on Ramsay Street. **Neighbours** makes babies happy say psychologists. Tests have shown that soap theme tunes soothe even unborn babies. **Neighbours** and EastEnders both have soothing theme tunes. The theory is that watching the shows during pregnancy relaxes the mothers; babies respond to sounds outside the womb after 14 weeks.

A recent survey of over 1,000 young adults aged 15 to 24 showed that an "outdoor Australian life" came above a "fast, New York yuppie life" in the popularity stakes.

Actor Stefan Dennis auditioned for the parts of Shane and Des before landing his role as Paul Robinson.

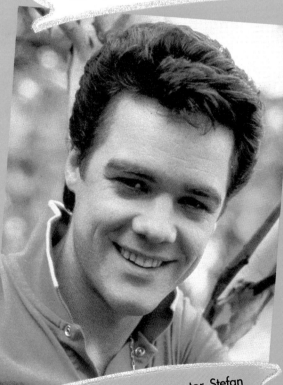

Lest they be forgotten... Bauer, Aldinger, Pierce — bet you won't recognize these names! They were the original neighbours whose houses are used for outdoor **Neighbours** shots. And how about Adrian van den Bok, Cheredith Mok, Ginny Lowndes and C.V. Schofield? No? They are all scriptwriters who have provided us with hours of **Neighbours** entertainment.

While becoming an actor Stefan Dennis trained as a chef. He would do stints in restaurants between jobs, or work weekends livening up the menu for patients in a geriatric hospital with French pastries and cakes.

# NEIGHBOURS GOSSIP

Have the paper hankies ready. Do you remember it? The Wedding! No, not Andy and Fergie – **The Wedding**! – Kylie and Jason, that is Scott and Charlene. I don't think life will ever be the same again!

So many false starts, so many obstacles – real and imagined. Will she? Won't she? Will he? Won't he? As they say, the path of true love never runs smoothly!

At times it seemed we were all holding our breath: Charlene storming off to live in the caravan. Was it really all over? Scott looking more and more confused and desperate. The adults taking it in turns to have tantrums. The solutions to each problem found . . . but which never worked.

Did you go misty-eyed when Madge so carefully produced her own wedding dress, and did you stamp your foot in frustration when it was discovered the dress was full of holes?

Did you gaze longingly with Charlene at the beautiful dress in the window, and then die with her when she went back and the dress was gone? Did you have problems deciding who to thump first? – Charlene's grandad muttering about the Robinsons, or Jim stalking off in solitary splendour to sulk.

How we all shed tears looking back to the romantic times when love was all, and obstacles were put there to be swept aside. Their wide-eyed trust in each other gave Charlene and Scott their place in popular history. Was there ever a love story we so badly wanted to end happily?

We couldn't even relax when we joined Scott at the church. Would there be another 'Daphne and Des' mishap? Would all the nervous males chicken out and succumb to large quantities of the amber nectar, and would all the females make yet another pot of tea, close the door, and put their feet up?

When Charlene finally arrived on Henry's arm she looked lovely. We wept and congratulated ourselves she had at last made it to the altar. Now life could get back to normal.

Except now there were other things to worry about. Would Scott successfully retake his exams and find a job as a reporter; how would Charlene's apprenticeship work out; would they manage to cope with next to no money . . . in short, would their marriage survive?

# BEAUTIFUL AUSTRALIA

## Home of the Rainbow Serpent

Ayers Rock is one of the wonders of the world, and certainly one of the best known places in Australia. Very close to the centre of the continent, 442km (275 miles) south-west of Alice Springs, Ayers Rock is over 500 million years old.

The first white man to discover it was William Gosse in 1873, and he named it after Sir Henry Ayers, then premier of South Australia. The rock was once part of a mountain range stretching east-west across Central Australia.

Among the most spectacular sights in Australia, Ayers Rock is over 300m (1000 feet) high and 8km (five miles) round. Rising like a great red block from the flat landscape, it can be seen 240km (150 miles) away as a low, purple mound on the horizon.

Few white visitors had seen it prior to 1930, and it was as recently as 1950 that the first organized party of tourists arrived. Nowadays there is a modern 5-star hotel as well as motels to stay at and there's a road where there used to be just desert. As a result the number of visitors has risen astronomically.

Close to, the rock is an awe-inspiring sight. Almost magically it changes colours as the sun moves over it, sometimes bright red, sometimes deep brown, sometimes almost black.

Ayers Rock was sacred to the Aborigines long before the white man arrived. The tribes of Central Australia would travel hundreds of miles to hold their ritual ceremonies at *Uluru* or 'the earth mother'.

A waterhole at the top was once, according to legend, the home of the Rainbow Serpent. This was one of the creator-spirits who had appeared from below the Earth at the beginning of time. All the natural features of the landscape — which before had been flat and empty — were made by these spirits. And, the Aborigines believe, the Rainbow Serpent is still there, once more asleep in the Earth.

Photos by courtesy of the Australian Tourist Commission

# RELUCTANT SUPERSTAR

Annie Jones

**Plain Jane Superbrain has emerged from behind those spots and spectacles to become the new glamour girl of Neighbours. Actress Annie Jones is taking it all in her stride.**

# "I'm very happy to be Annie Jones"

"Jane's a goody-goody," laughs Annie. "She's not a bit like me. I get angry and I get mad because I'm a real human being." Her on-screen personality is a big hit with viewers though, and Jane is all set to move into the limelight now that Charlene has vacated the spot.

"Once Kylie Minogue flew the coop," explained producer Mark Callan, "we were forced to take another look at Mrs Mangel's grand-daughter." The result is a bigger starring role in the soap for Jane.

"I find the whole suggestion that I should be the next Kylie Minogue very insulting," says Annie. "There is no need for me to be the next anyone. I have absolutely no desire to be anything other than what I am. I'm very happy to be Annie Jones. I'm very lucky. I don't get any hassle at all from fans. In Kylie's shoes I'd get triple the amount. Even Kylie admits she can't cope with the pressure at times."

Off the screen Annie is rather shy and prefers not to be interviewed by the media. But despite her shyness, Annie admits she gave the producers of **Neighbours** a very tough time.

"I pestered and pestered the production company to get a part," she says. "I had appeared on several other Australian TV shows but desperately wanted to get into

**Neighbours**. So for two months I kept ringing up the show's bosses just to remind them that I was alive and wanted to join them. I think in the end they gave me a job just to keep me quiet."

She was given the small part of schoolgirl Jane Harris for a planned six weeks of appearances. The TV company has held on to her ever since.

While she waited for her big break Annie worked in Melbourne's boutiques, restaurants, and as a cocktail waitress. "I can mix a pretty mean cocktail," she laughs.

"**Neighbours** is very tiring," she says, "but we're producing two and a half hours of television a week. Fishing is my relaxation. I adore all the peace and quiet that goes with angling. I got the bug from my father."

Accompanying her on these trips is boyfriend Paul, a film and television director. Annie currently shares a two-bedroomed cottage with him in a yuppie area of West Melbourne.

Unlike many Australians, she has no desire to travel to London. "If I went overseas now I'd go to a place where they don't have **Neighbours** — like Africa," she says. And what of her future? "I guess my long-term plan is just to stay in work. I'll be quite satisfied with that!"

# "I desperately wanted to get into Neighbours"

# LOVE THY Neighbours

# EPISODE ONE

*Mrs Mangel is worried about Jane, Henry has a scheme for which he needs Mike and Jane, and Bouncer has a frisbee . . .*

"It's really very good of you to call in," said Nell Mangel, adjusting the cushions behind her on the settee.

Harold Bishop beamed happily. "Shall I pour?" he asked, leaning forward to pick up the teapot. "I've made you camomile. I hope that's to your liking, Mrs Mangel. And I took the liberty of bringing over some carrot cake I baked especially."

"You have impeccable taste, Mr Bishop," said Mrs Mangel. "You're most kind. This is altogether most pleasant. It's true I am only feeling a little off colour, but these kindnesses mean so much when one is not in the best of health."

"Indeed, Mrs Mangel," agreed Harold. "Where would we be without the civilizing habit of taking afternoon tea with our friends and neighbours?"

"I couldn't agree more," replied Mrs Mangel, watching Harold fill the cups and hand one to her. She paused thoughtfully for a few moments. "I was wondering, now that you're here – "

"Yes?" prompted Harold, ever eager to be of service.

"There is something that's troubling me," Mrs Mangel continued. "Of course, I don't want to burden you with my problems . . . "

"Think nothing of it," beamed Harold expansively, adding in haste, "not that I would think for a moment that you could be a burden, Mrs Mangel, of course. How can I be of service?"

"You're a man of the world, Mr Bishop."

Harold flushed slightly at the compliment.

"Well," Mrs Mangel went on, leaning forward in a conspiratorial manner as if she feared being overheard, "you know that I am the last person to spread gossip."

Harold smiled sheepishly. This wasn't entirely his view, since Mrs Mangel was renowned the length of Ramsay Street for being to rumours what spies are to state secrets. Experience, however, had taught him that discretion was the better part of valour as far as Mrs Mangel went, so he remained silent.

"But when rumours affect one personally,"

Bouncer came out the easy winner. Clearly feeling this was a great game, the big dog clamped his jaws on the bright, red plastic disc and made his escape.

"Grab him, Henry!" yelled Mike.

Henry's arms clutched at thin air, and he, Mike and Jane watched as Bouncer disappeared across the park.

"After him!" shouted Jane, and, laughing, the three of them set off in pursuit of Bouncer, calling out his name as they ran.

Ten minutes of sprinting, diving and shouting later, Jane, Mike and Henry were lying exhausted on the grass. Bouncer, bored now that he'd been left to play by himself, trotted over amiably, gnawing enthusiastically at the frisbee.

Hoping to encourage further sport he dropped the chewed, wet frisbee on Mike's chest, and sat back expectantly. Mike sat up and examined what was left of the thing. There were deep teeth marks all round the edge, and Bouncer had managed to tear out a sizeable chunk from the frisbee. It was definitely an ex-frisbee now.

"Well, that's the end of that," he said. "Here, Bouncer, it's all yours." He threw the frisbee in the air, and watched as it plummeted unimpressively to the ground a short distance away. Bouncer was off like a shot. "Anyone fancy something to drink?" asked Mike. "I'm parched."

"I can't stay long," said Jane. "Nan's not too well today, and she's expecting me back any time now."

"Relax," said Henry, "we're not about to kidnap you for the white slave trade. Besides, I've got a scheme I wanted to fill you both in on. We'll have a quick coffee and then deliver you home safe and sound. Your gran can't object to that, surely?"

Mrs Mangel went on, "one cannot ignore them. I'm telling you this in the strictest confidence, naturally, Mr Bishop."

"You can rely on me," said Harold. "Now what exactly is the trouble?"

"It's Jane," she said simply. "I'm very worried about Jane."

Bouncer barked happily and raced off in hot pursuit of the flying frisbee Jane had just thrown. Henry caught it expertly, stepping backwards to intercept its flight one-handed. He failed to notice the recently dug hole that Bouncer had been excavating just before the game.

Over went his ankle just as the big, playful dog bounded up to him. With Bouncer going at full tilt just at the moment Henry overbalanced, man, dog and frisbee collapsed in a heap on the grass.

"What I object to," Mrs Mangel was saying, "is the kind of company Jane is keeping. I wouldn't for a moment hold Henry Ramsay's past record against him, but a criminal record is a criminal record after all."

"Deep down he has a conscience."

*Stefan Dennis*, on Paul

Harold was about to interrupt in Henry's defence but Mrs Mangel swept on immediately. "And I know Mike is a nice enough young man – very personable, as we would have said in my day – but – "

"But?" said Harold, wondering what was going to come next. Mrs Mangel hardly seemed to hear him.

"Jane's not had the happiest of upbringings, as you know," she went on. "And I blame myself for the way her mother has shunned her maternal responsibilities."

"Quite unjustly, if I may say so, Mrs Mangel," commented Harold, honestly. "Whatever Jane might at one time have lacked, you have more than amply provided. Her upbringing – "

"Precisely, Mr Bishop," said Mrs Mangel, not bothering to wait for him to finish. "Jane's upbringing has been my responsibility. I've always done my best for her, and if we've not always seen eye to eye, I've only done what I thought was best for Jane." She paused to take a sip of tea. "I suppose I'd hoped my influence might help her rise above her background. After all, Jane is an extremely bright and intelligent girl, and – no disrespect to Mike or, er, Henry – frankly she deserves better. From what I hear she's spending an unhealthy amount of time in their company."

Harold was at a loss for words for a few seconds. "I'm sure you're worrying needlessly, Mrs Mangel. I believe you'll find they're both good friends to Jane, and only have her best interests at heart."

Mrs Mangel remained unconvinced. "I only wish I had your confidence, Mr Bishop."

"Taking time off from the heady world of high finance, Des?" inquired Henry cheerily as he approached the counter.

Des Clarke looked up, and was about to answer sharply when he spotted Mike tying up Bouncer before coming into the Coffee Shop. A second later Mike and Jane came through the door.

"Look, I know you're busy, Mike," he said, his voice agitated, "but you did say you'd be here half an hour ago. I've had to stand in for you – I told you Harold was taking a couple of hours off this afternoon. Madge is filling in in the kitchen, but she can't be expected to run the place all by herself."

"Sorry, Des," apologized Mike. "It went clean out of my head. Here, let me take over." He moved round behind the counter. "Leave it to me, Des, you get off."

"Right. Thanks, Mike," said Des, swapping the apron for his jacket. "See you later at the house." He was gone before Mike could reply.

Mike went into the small kitchen. Madge was busy at the stove.

"Don't apologize," said Madge, before Mike could say a word. "Harold has left everything prepared. I am perfectly capable of looking

"I had enough of my shirts being ripped off my back."

*Peter O'Brien,* on the public life of a soap superstar

23

after things. Besides, it's quiet this afternoon. Des is just panicking for no good reason."

"He's still under a lot of strain," observed Mike.

Madge stopped what she was doing and sighed. "All the more reason for you to keep your promises, Mike. You don't get over losing someone that close overnight."

"I guess we just have to give him time," reflected Mike, "and offer what support we can. He has his up days as well as his downs. Des is a survivor."

"A lot of it's been because of his good friends," said Madge warmly, "like you and Jane and Henry."

"We all try to do our best to help one another, don't we, Mrs Bishop?" said Mike modestly.

"Well, most of us do," said Madge, raising an eyebrow. She turned back to the stove. "Des thinks the world of you, you know, Mike. More than ever now. And he relies on you."

"I know."

"Don't take it personally if he flies off the handle now and then," continued Madge. "It's a strange thing losing someone very close to you." She stirred the sauce slowly and rhythmically. "You feel all kinds of emotions — sadness, fear, loneliness, anger, sometimes a complete numbness. And it takes time for the shock to wear off. You need patient and loving friends."

Madge tapped the wooden spoon against the side of the saucepan. "There, that should do it," she said, lowering the heat. She turned to Mike. "We all try to understand how you'll be feeling still. What I mean to say is, don't feel Des is your sole responsibility. The rest of us are here to help as well. Take it easy on yourself."

Mike smiled. "I'm fine, Mrs Bishop, really, but yes, I will." He went back into the coffee shop and took his place behind the counter.

"Service around here is shocking," said Henry. "I think I should complain to the management."

"I am the management this afternoon," said Mike. "Now would you like to make a complaint or order a drink?"

"Something long and cold," said Henry.

"A hot drink's better for you," said Jane.

"In this weather? You've got to be joking!" said Henry. "Long and cold for me."

"She's right," said Mike. "It's a scientific fact. It lowers your body temperature more efficiently."

Henry took this in, thought carefully for a few moments, and then a broad grin spread across his face. "That's good. That's good. It fits in perfectly."

"Wait a minute," said Jane. "What fits in where?"

Henry reached out and touched Mike and Jane. "You lucky people are in on the start of something really big."

Mike and Jane exchanged a glance that had 'big debts' written all over it.

"Okay," said Mike good-humouredly, "so long as you don't want me to sign anything. What's the great idea, Henry?"

"How much is it going to cost us?" asked Jane more directly.

Henry made a show of being hurt. "Do I look as if I'm after your money?" He assumed the most angelic look he could muster.

"Yes," said Mike and Jane together.

"That's not fair!" complained Henry.

"So how much is it going to cost us?" asked Mike.

"Nothing," said Henry. "Well, no capital outlay as such. That is, minimal."

"How much, Henry?" persisted Jane.

"A few dollars here and there for publicity," said Henry. "Some handbills. Nothing more. Maybe some application forms, membership cards, invoices, that kind of normal, office

stuff. Small things, one or two essential items – that's all. Peanuts compared to the earning growth potential of this idea. You're going to love it!"

Henry's wave of enthusiasm crashed not altogether effectively against the steep cliffs of Mike and Jane's suspicion.

Mike eyed Henry closely. "So what's the catch? What is this great idea that costs next to nothing and is going to make us the Erinsborough millionaires overnight?"

Henry allowed a dramatic silence to settle, and then announced, "An entirely new concept in canine fitness services . . . dog-orobics!"

Mike and Jane stared at each other in puzzled amusement. Jane spoke first, stifling a giggle. "You mean like dog biscuits: dogo-bics?"

"No, no," said Henry. "Dog-orobics, like in aerobics, only it's for dogs, see."

"Are you serious?" asked Mike.

"How much?" repeated Jane.

"Two hundred dollars should do it," said Henry.

"He's serious," said Jane.

The stones sparkled in the bright shafts of afternoon sunlight. The light refracted through them, bouncing sparkling rays of colour into the air.

"A truly beautiful piece, Mrs Mangel," said Harold, handing it back carefully to her. "A very fine brooch indeed."

"It was my grandmother's originally," explained Mrs Mangel. "It's very dear to me. I've saved it for Jane as a gift on the occasion of her engagement." She slipped the brooch back into its small velvet bag.

"A delightful gesture, Mrs Mangel," said Harold with feeling.

"As you know, Mr Bishop, I'm not a wealthy woman, but the few special things I do have to pass on, well, I'd like to make sure they were going to the right people," said Mrs Mangel.

"Come, come," said Harold, "there's no

"Such a frigid cow, this old bird."

*Myra de Groot,*
on Eileen Clarke

need to be so morbid. There's years left in the old – " he hesitated just in time – "years left in the, er, bank yet."

"You never know when the hand of God may reach down, Mr Bishop, and pluck me away," said Mrs Mangel with great authority. "The unseen world is full of things we cannot see."

"True, true," said Harold, showing the white flag. Mrs Mangel had an answer for everything. "That'll be why it's called the unseen world, I expect, because we can't see it."

"Exactly my point, Mr Bishop," she replied. "I knew you'd understand, a man of your mature years and experience. You see, it's Jane."

"Yes," nodded Harold, recalling vaguely that Jane had been the original subject of the conversation, back in the distant past. He glanced at his watch out of the corner of his eye.

"I want the best for Jane. I've brought her up as well as I can. Goodness knows, Len was never very much help. She deserves a good life."

"And I'm sure she'll find it, Mrs Mangel," said Harold. "You've given her a fine start in life, if I may say so. A firm but loving hand."

She interrupted him. "I don't mean to belittle Mike in any way, but I feel Jane is destined to reach higher. I feel it, Mr Bishop."

Harold shrugged. "And how does the brooch – "

"Goodness, is that the time?" said Mrs Mangel suddenly. "You really shouldn't keep me talking like this, Mr Bishop. Jane ought to have been home half an hour ago. Where can she have got to? She only took Bouncer for a walk." Her words came out at some speed, as her mind went into top gear. The genuine and immediate concern for her grand-daughter showed plainly on her face.

"I'm sure she hasn't come to any harm," said Harold.

"Excuse me, Mr Bishop," said Mrs Mangel, "I can't sit here and worry. I have to go out and look for her. She may be lying injured in a road somewhere."

"But you're not well," protested Harold to no avail. "I'll come with you," he added immediately, following in her footsteps as she swept past him.

They had barely entered the park when they saw Jane and Bouncer in the distance. Mike was with them.

Harold waved a friendly welcome and the figures drew closer. Harold was smiling, and he was about to point out that there had been no need to worry, as he had predicted, when a voice like thunder burst out beside him.

"And just where do you think you've been, Jane?" demanded Mrs Mangel. "I've been very worried indeed. Ask Mr Bishop." Harold stood his ground, open-mouthed.

"It was my fault, Mrs Mangel," said Mike. "We were going over this scheme of Henry's – "

"I might have known!" she said crossly. "And look at the state poor Bouncer's in. You've worn him out. Really Jane, I expected better of you."

With that she whisked Jane away with Bouncer following in their wake. Harold, still slightly dazed, half turned to go after them, then changed his mind.

"Thank you for the tea," he called lamely after Mrs Mangel's departing figure. There was no reply. He swung round to face Mike. They shrugged shoulders. "Now then, Mike," said Harold, taking Mike gently by the arm, "what scheme of Henry's would this be?"

*Episode Two continues on Page 34*

"It portrays a white middle-class society and has very little to do with the realities of life in Melbourne where one person in four lives mainly on state benefit, where teenage unemployment runs at 20 per cent and where one fifth of the population regularly speak a language other than English."

Ruth Brown in *The Guardian*

# BEAUTIFUL AUSTRALIA

## The Place of Many Heads

As you wrap that warm cardigan round you and draw closer to the fire, remember that Australia is the world's leading producer of wool. She exports 95% of all the wool she produces. Merinos are the most populous sheep, a breed especially selected for its ability to survive extremely dry conditions.

The merinos were introduced in the 19th century, and bred from an original flock owned by George III. They started their life down under on a 2,000 acre area near Mount Taurus, in New South Wales. The place was, rather unromantically, called the Cowpastures, but later renamed Camden.

Twenty years later a flock of saxon merinos were landed, which proved even hardier than their Spanish cousins. All the major bloodlines of today's Australian sheep began with these two flocks.

Modern sheep farming is done on huge farms, called stations, covering 100,000 acres or more. These are concentrated more in the temperate south, while cattle are favoured in the sub-tropical north.

So, the next time you can't sleep, just think of Australia... and start counting!

All Australia's major cities and towns are on or near the coast. The vast continent's interior, the outback, is vast. You're more likely to bump into a sheep than a human being in many places, and the spirits of the Dreamtime are everywhere...

Among the many stunning sights to be seen in the Northern Territory is Mount Olga. It is, in fact, a whole series of peaks, thirty amazing domes, covering twenty five acres. For the local Aborigines it is *Katijula*, meaning 'many heads'.

These heads belong to the spirit people who made the land in the beginning, and who sleep here now in the eternal Dreamtime. Mount Olga lies to the west of Ayers Rock, one of three peaks whose eastern end is Mount Conner.

It was named after the Queen of Spain by the explorer Ernest Giles in 1872. He described his first view of it this way: "The appearance of this mountain is marvellous in the extreme, and baffles accurate description....it displayed to our astonished eyes rounded minarets, giant cupolas, and monstrous domes."

Photos by courtesy of the Australian Tourist Commission

# MR NICE GUY

**Handsome, British-born Guy Pearce has worked hard for his success. And personal tragedies in his life have been part of the motivation for him to do well.**

## "I train up to 20 hours a week"

Hard times are not a new thing to Guy. He lost his father when he was only eight years old. "I remember the actual day," he recalls. "My mum had to break the news to me. I didn't crack up and turn into an emotional wreck but I did sit and wonder whether life was fair. At least I was old enough to remember my dad with affection."

The second family tragedy is that Guy's 22-year-old sister, Tracy, is mentally retarded. "She's like a ten-year-old," says Guy sadly, "but she's wonderful. She's my greatest fan. She loves asking people, 'Do you watch my brother?' She has lived at home all her life until recently when she moved to a place where she can be semi-independent with several others who are the same. I try and get to see her every five or six weeks."

The only other girl in Guy's life is steady girlfriend, Shaney. They have been together for a couple of years. "She's a child care assistant," explains Guy, "and what I liked about her is that I had to do the chasing. We met at one of the promotional appearances we do for **Neighbours**, and she wasn't one of the girls who rushed up wanting an autograph. She's a lovely girl and we're pretty serious about each other. But at the moment we don't live together."

A former holder of the Victoria Teenage Body Builder title, Mike keeps himself in good shape. "I used to weigh only 10 stone, but now I'm about 12 stone. Once I'm in the gym I find it hard to stop and sometimes I train up to 20 hours a week. The last thing I want to do is show half the world an awful-looking body!"

Apart from his **Neighbours** success, Guy is hoping to hit the big time as a musician. "I've always been interested in music and I've been writing songs for over seven years," he says. "I must have written over 300 by now. I played the sax for seven years at school and I've taught myself the piano on an old upright. I had a couple of bands through school and now I would love to make records. But I'm quite serious about it. I don't want people to say I'm only doing it because I'm in **Neighbours** and got a recording contract."

Whatever his future brings, Guy can be sure that his family is closely behind him in all he does. "When I started out acting I think my mum was worried. She really wanted me to go to university and study. But now I think she is happy. She sees that I am coping well."

## "I would love to make records"

## Mark Little

Mark Little leads a double life. On the one hand he is Joe Mangel, Mrs Mangel's son and brother to Jane's mother, rough diamond and lovable rogue rolled into one. On the other hand he is Proton, a futuristic being who has been given the job of ending the universe using high-impact aerobics. It just depends on where you see Joe.

As well as being a regular member of **Neighbours**, Mark is also committed to continuing to work in live theatre. But his stage persona is a million miles away from brickie Joe, as any of the show's fans will have discovered if they caught Mark's act at the Melbourne Comedy Festival.

"I expect they'll get a hell of a shock when they see my stand-up work," warns Mark with a mischievous smile. "**Neighbours** is television land — reactionary sort of stuff — whereas my comedy work is a lot more anarchic. I'm an anarchic humorist. Most of my jokes have a political basis, a reaction to what's happening around me."

In collaboration with fellow actor Anthony Morgan, Mark has put together a show called *The Adventurers*, which enables them to make comments on a wide number of important issues . . . and entertain at the same time.

"We always try to present comedy in a different way to the norm," Mark explains. "This show is not just a series of comedians standing up and doing a night of jokes and sketches, and it's not a comedy play either . . . I suppose you could say it's funny experimental theatre. We're trying to drag comedy out of a rut, presenting a comedy night in a different way to the usual format."

Little and Morgan have earned themselves a reputation as the bad boys of

### "I'm an anarchic humorist"

# MAKING THEIR MARK

the comedy circuit, a title that Mark appears to relish. With a grin, he adds, "We've both been banned from about the same number of venues." So maybe Joe and Mark do have a little something in common after all.

Mark Stevens couldn't be further from the character of Nick Page if he tried. The street wise graffiti artist is not a role model Mark would like his young fans to follow.

Tearaway Nick is constantly in trouble for pointing his spray can at walls that don't belong to him, although Mark admits a grudging admiration for some street graffiti. "I like the bright, beautiful ones," he says. "Some of them are quite brilliant. But I don't like the junk ones like those which say get someone out of jail.

"I certainly don't want people to copy Nick," Mark adds quickly. "He's a rough boy and you have to earn his respect, but he's settling down a bit."

**Neighbours** is Mark's first acting role, although he already has quite extensive television experience with three years on *Young Talent Time*. "I just did a screen test," he explains, "and the next thing I knew I had the part. It came at a good time because I had just grown out of *Young Talent Time*.

Mark appears to have made the transition with ease. "Luckily, I don't have trouble learning lines — I'm used to learning 10 songs a week for *Young Talent Time*. I just read the lines at home, look them over before I go on and that's it."

One experience Mark did have a little trouble preparing himself for — a screen romance with Sharon Davies. "It's my first kissing scenes this week," he revealed before shooting, "and I'm a bit nervous." Just so long as Ramsay Street doesn't start sprouting 'Nick Loves Sharon True' graffiti!

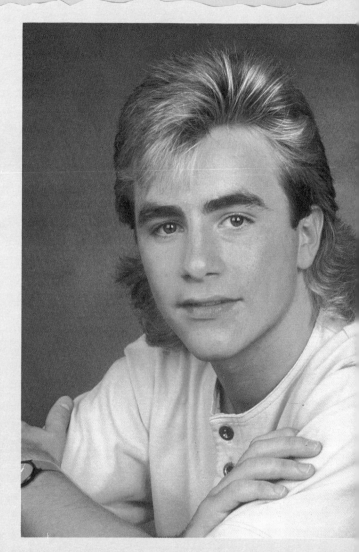

## Mark Stevens

## "I certainly don't want people to copy Nick"

# AUSTRALIA'S BEST-KNOWN DAD

Alan Dale

"The most beautiful woman I have ever seen"

**Alan Dale has a lot in common with friendly Jim Robinson, but life wasn't always so sweet for the ex-milkman from New Zealand. His current happiness owes much to a former Miss Australia.**

Alan is all too familiar with the problems that faced Scott and Charlene in their marriage. He married his childhood sweetheart, Clare, and like Scott he met with firm opposition from his parents. "Everyone told us we were too young. I was 21 and Clare was 17 and very beautiful. But we wouldn't listen. You don't at that age, do you?"

Alan can talk wisely about it now, but at the time life was a struggle for the aspiring actor. "I had a wife and two children to support," says Alan of those early days, and acting took a back seat to selling cars, and later running a milk round while he studied at law school.

Then came the first big break when Alan talked his way into a DJ's job on a local radio station. In 1979 he decided it was time to make a move, and with just ten dollars in his pocket he set off for Australia. Less than two weeks later he had landed a part in *The Young Doctors*.

But success had its price. Alan and Clare split up, and a divorce followed a couple of years later. As he became a star, so Alan found himself in the company of some of Australia's most glamorous women. It wasn't until 1984, however, that Alan was to meet the woman who has since made his success complete.

"The second I set eyes on Tracey I fell totally in love," says Alan. "She is the most beautiful woman I have ever seen in my life." Hardly surprising that Alan's praise should be so fulsome — Tracey was the winner of the coveted Miss Australia title.

Tracey says, "I admired him. He was fun to go out with. But we didn't rush into a relationship." 42-year-old Alan was painfully aware of their age difference. Tracey is twenty years his junior, and only slightly older than his two sons, Matthew (20) and Simon (17).

At first when Tracey moved to Melbourne to be near Alan, she had her own flat but admitted that her cat had moved in with Alan, and within the year Tracey followed. Alan, Tracey and the two boys now live together in a detached, five-bedroomed Victorian house, lavishly decorated with ironwork, in an exclusive Melbourne suburb.

"I'm a solo mum," says Alan, "and a feminist. But life as a single parent hasn't been easy, although the housework has always gone smoothly. When the boys first arrived from New Zealand I sat them down and said, 'Okay, I respect your desire to be here and I love you and want you here. But the deal is that there are three of us here, and it's everyone together if there's shopping, cooking or sweeping to do.' The boys made it possible for it not to be so difficult because they cook as much as I do."

Alan admits however, "There were times when having a mother there would have made a lot of difference."

The boys seem to have no complaints. "Dad's very positive," says Matthew. "Just being around him helps us to be successful as well. He keeps us going every step of the way."

Tracey agrees enthusiastically. "Alan helps keep me up all the time. I've never met anyone before who did that."

Alan himself is characteristically modest and down-to-earth. "I'm not too keen on being asked for my autograph," he says. "I've always found it a very sobering experience because it makes me realize how fickle fame is. One minute you can be at the top of the tree, the next you can be down and out. To keep my feet on the ground I always ask fans for their autograph in return!"

**"I'm a solo mum and a feminist"**

# LOVE THY
## Neighbours

*Henry has devised some madcap scheme to do with dogs, and Jane is in her nan's bad books. Harold is doing his best to advise Mrs Mangel, and generally keep the peace . . . but for how long?*

## EPISODE TWO

"Isn't she dreadful – thank goodness she doesn't live near me."

*Vivean Gray,* on Mrs Mangel

The dawn of another day brought a sunlit morning. Away in the distance a bubble of cloud hovered on the horizon, but it was a long way off. The sunshine felt good on Harold's face as he crossed Ramsay Street and approached Mrs Mangel's front door.

She answered the doorbell dressed ready for work in her Lassiters' uniform. "Ah, Mr Bishop, good morning."

"Good morning, Mrs Mangel," he replied. "I hope you won't think me forward, but I was a little concerned yesterday evening when we parted and . . ."

"Your concern is gratefully acknowledged," said Mrs Mangel, "but, as you can see, everything is fine, thank you, Mr Bishop. I was about to leave for work." Harold wondered if he saw her hand tremble for a moment as she held on to the door frame, but her eyes fixed his firmly. "Was there anything else?"

"As a matter of fact there was," said Harold.

"I was thinking about that brooch you showed me, and it occurred to me that if it was of any value – "

"My thoughts entirely," interjected Mrs Mangel. "Now – "

" – that you shouldn't keep it around the house," continued Harold resolutely. "It would be much safer in a bank. You should have a word with Des about it. I'm sure he'd tell you the same thing."

"Of course, you're right, Mr Bishop. I'm afraid I'm not thinking straight at the moment. I'll call in to see him today."

Jane appeared at that moment and uttered an abrupt, "Excuse me," before walking between her grandmother and Harold.

"Good morning, Jane," said Harold brightly.

"Good morning, Mr Bishop," said Jane quietly, without looking up. She went down the path. Before Harold could turn and pursue the matter Mrs Mangel spoke.

"I do think **Neighbours** is a very good programme, although it is fashionable to be snooty about it. But I have nothing but contempt for *EastEnders.*"

*Mary Whitehouse*

"I'm afraid you'll have to excuse me too. I don't want to be late for work. I have an example to set. Good morning."

"Good morning," said Harold as the door closed. As he strolled back home he began to doubt if it was such a wonderful morning after all. On the horizon the clouds seemed barely to have encroached on the broad, blue sky. Harold hummed something stirring to himself to restore his spirits.

When he walked into the kitchen he was glad he had. Henry was sitting eating his breakfast at the table.

Harold cleared his throat. "Ah Henry, just the man I wanted to see."

Henry paused between mouthfuls. "Really?"

Harold approached the table and sat down. "I didn't have an opportunity to speak to you last night. It's about this idea of yours. I wasn't too sure about it."

"About the name, right? Dog-orobics. I see what Jane means. It makes you think of dog biscuits. Not the right image at all. I was thinking of changing it. What do you think about Dog and Jog, something like that?"

"That's not my point, Henry," said Harold.

"Your mother and I have talked this over, and we feel the idea, er, needs more thought."

Henry put down his spoon and leaned across the table towards Harold. "That's the beauty of it, Harold, don't you see? It's so simple. People are into fitness right now, right?"

Harold nodded his cautious agreement.

"But people also lead busy lives, okay?" continued Henry. "These people who like to keep fit, also like their dogs to be fit and healthy. All too often they're too busy though. That's where I come in. It's a whole new, untapped market – we don't just walk the dogs, we provide aerobics for dogs!"

Harold listened patiently. He knew better than to rush these things. "Yes, I see that," he said simply. "Really, um, really quite novel. And how were you intending to run this, er, Dog and Jog company?"

"That's the neat part," said Henry enthusiastically. "I have Mike as my scientific adviser – well, he's going to Uni isn't he? He knows all about blood circulation and that kind of stuff. That always impresses the punters, having special advisers. And Jane,

"Even *Crossroads* was expensive by comparison."

**Neighbours** spokesperson

she's going to be my health and fitness consultant."

Harold took this in. "And your role in all this is?"

"Oh, I'll be taking the dog-orobic classes," said Henry proudly. "Are you really interested, Harold? I could cut you in on a piece of the action, as say a sleeping partner."

"Hold your horses, Henry — or should I say dogs?" said Harold. "If you'll take my advice I feel we ought perhaps to think this one through a little first."

"Is this a private party, or can anyone join in?"

Mike and Jane looked up to see Henry approaching over the little bridge as they sat outside the Coffee Shop. He joined them at their table, pulling up a chair. Mike and Jane didn't react.

"Did I say something?" asked Henry, incredulous.

A cloud passed over the face of the sun, momentarily sending Jane's features into cool shadow. She certainly looked a bit daggy, concluded Henry. Being a gentleman (when he remembered) he didn't say anything, but asked, "So who's died? Did somebody forget

to tell me something?"

"It's dog-orobics," began Mike.

"No, no, it's all right, I thought of a new name," enthused Henry. "Dogibodicare. No? How about Dog and Jog?"

"It's not that, Henry," said Jane. "Nan's forbidden me from having anything more to do with it."

Mike went on, "Jane got into a lot of trouble last night for being late."

"And Nan says I mistreated Bouncer," added Jane. "She says I'm the last person to be made responsible for a dog."

Henry mused, "Isn't that a bit over the top? I mean you haven't stolen the Crown Jewels or anything, have you?"

"Maybe your nan will simmer down in a day or two," suggested Mike hopefully.

"Yeah, that's right," said Henry, backing him up. "Besides, it'll give us time to put the finishing touches to the idea, put a few ideas down on paper, make her see it's a serious business proposition. She might even want to invest. I reckon I've got Harold interested already."

"Er, Henry," interrupted Mike, "one thing at a time, okay? Anyway we don't have the money. Let's just cool it for a day or two, maybe give it some more thought, like you say."

"That's exactly what Harold said," replied Henry.

"See?" said Jane. "Great minds think alike. We're all agreed. Let's just think about it for a bit. I can't afford to get into any more trouble right now."

Henry nodded and turned to Mike. "So what does Des have to say on the subject? You've told him all about it, yeah?"

Mike shifted uncomfortably in his seat. "Well, no not yet, Henry. To be honest with you I had a few second thoughts myself about the idea."

"Such as?" demanded Henry, sensing a rebellion brewing.

"Don't get me wrong," protested Mike. "It's a great idea."

"It deals with social problems. It's not heavy but it's relevant."

*Alan Dale*

"Great idea," echoed Jane.

"But?" inquired Henry.

"But – " said Jane.

"But we don't think it's going to work," said Mike.

Henry couldn't believe his ears. This was mutiny in the ranks, the great dog-orobics empire crumbling in his very fingers. He stood up and pushed his chair back defiantly.

"I see which way the wind blows," he said, looking at the two of them meaningfully. "Backing out just when I'm getting the thing off the ground. Okay, so who needs you? I'll do it myself. You'll see. I'll get the money together on my own, and it'll work. Right?"

"Henry," pleaded Jane as Henry resolutely turned his back on them and marched away.

"He'll get over it," said Mike. "This time next week it'll be some new scheme for washing people's tropical fish, or talking to people's plants to keep them happy while their owners are at work."

"Perhaps you're right," laughed Jane.

"I am," smiled Mike. "We've heard the last of dog-orobics."

Des Clarke rose from behind his desk and crossed the room to open the door of his office. "We'll take care of that for you, Mrs Mangel," he was saying. "I entirely agree with you that a safety deposit box is by far the wisest course of action."

"I'm so grateful for your help, Mr Clarke," she said.

"No trouble at all," smiled Des. "If you bring the item in we'll lock it safely away, and issue you with a key."

"And I can see it whenever I want?"

"Any time at all – within banking hours," Des reassured her. "And if you amend your will then the key will pass safely to Jane, and the brooch will be hers."

Des took the opportunity to open the door. He was already ten minutes behind with his next appointment, but Mrs Mangel had insisted on giving him the whole story. He smiled again patiently.

"Thank you again, Mr Clarke," she said. "Goodbye."

"Goodbye," said Des, surprised now the moment had actually come. In the middle of a conversation with Nell Mangel, he reflected, you could feel stranded a million miles from anywhere, with the end completely out of sight.

Des went back into the office and sat down. He suddenly realized how grateful he was after all for people like Mrs Mangel. She might not always have the most important things to say. There were plenty of things over which Des knew he would most certainly be in disagreement with her.

But it had been the willingness of people to talk to him, to bring him back from the brink, that had helped him stay together after losing Daphne. Close friends, neighbours, had not let him go down, and Mrs Mangel had been amongst them. "Yes." He found himself smiling. "I have to admit it, I'm glad the old battleaxe is around."

There was a tap on the door, and Nell Mangel's head appeared from behind it. "There was just one more thing . . . "

"Sometimes I'm glad," Des murmured silently to himself. "Sometimes."

"Actually I think it would be quite easy for me to live here permanently."

*Anne Charleston*, on Britain

Jane relaxed on the settee, watching a video. It was an old film Harold had rented and insisted her grandmother should watch. Another time Jane might have appreciated a classic French production of Victor Hugo's *Les Miserables* with sub-titles, but today was not the day. She was miserable enough already.

She hadn't seen her grandmother since they'd parted with such hostility after breakfast. But when Nan had started criticizing her choice of friends Jane had seen red; her nan could be such a terrible snob at times . . . suggesting Jane was too good for Mike or Henry. It made her blood boil!

At that instant the doorbell rang. Opening the door, Jane saw Henry standing before her, looking apologetic and innocent.

"I've come to say I'm sorry," he said simply, and handed her a bunch of flowers. If Jane didn't know better she could have sworn she'd seen flowers very like these in the garden of a house further along Ramsay Street.

She ushered him in and returned to the sofa. Great numbers of French peasants being miserable radiated out at them from the video. Jane flipped the remote control.

"Don't switch it off on my account," said Henry. "Not if you like that sort of thing. Anyway," he added quickly, before she changed her mind, "I came here to say I'm sorry, and to say I have an idea that I think will solve everything. Trust me."

"Henry," began Jane uncertainly. "Apology accepted, but – "

"Can you come to the park now?" interjected Henry. "This will only take half an hour."

"Now?" said Jane. "Nan will – " She paused a second, realizing she was almost glad of the excuse to delay meeting her nan. "I can leave her a note, tell her where I've gone, what time I'll be back."

She didn't feel good about going against her nan, but she felt she had to make some sort of stand about her choice of friends. She scribbled a quick note. "Shall we take Bouncer?"

"Better not," said Henry. "Let's not tempt fate. But you'll need your coat. I think it might rain before too long."

"Hold on a second," said Jane. "It's in the bedroom." Two minutes later they were striding their way to the park.

The first heavy drops of rain were beginning to fall as Nell Mangel reached the welcoming sight of her front door. She felt unusually tired. The day had been a strain, and the bad feeling between herself and Jane troubled her.

The thought of the brooch brought a resurgence of pleasure. She entered the house, and went directly to the brooch's safe hiding place.

Her heart missed a beat. It wasn't there. The box was empty with no sign of the brooch or its velvet bag. "I must be losing my senses," she chided herself. "I didn't put it back after I showed it to Mr Bishop yesterday."

But it wasn't on the settee either, or on the table, the floor, or anywhere else she looked. Ouside the rain began to beat down with a steady, incessant roar. In Ramsay Street itself, Beverly Robinson was driving home from her day's work at the hospital.

She looked across to see the figure of Mrs Mangel appear at her doorway and then stumble. Beverly slammed on the brakes and leapt from the car. Nell Mangel lay perfectly still on the wet ground, not moving.

*Episode Three continues on Page 50*

"**Neighbours** is quite suitable as a family programme. Children find it entertaining, and parents find it a useful programme to watch with their children . . . it tackles emotional problems without embarrassment. It has very strong storylines and is quite simple . . . that's why children watch it."

*Anna Home,*
Head of BBC Children's Programmes

# NEIGHBOURS SEARCH-A-WORD

The neighbours have got themselves jumbled up!
You can help straighten them out by finding where
the words listed below are hidden in the grid. All
the words are in straight lines but may read up or
down, backwards or forwards or even diagonally.

```
S E K R O C A N O I F P O H S T
S C Y R A H C S C H A R L E N E
R E O P A U L K E A N E T G E R
E G I T S T L N X D C L O N N I
D N K L T K R J Y K O P P A A N
N A K O E Y Y N A N F E M I J S
A M I K E E O A I H F G I T A B
L E N A H S N X S A S D B S N O
E G I S N D E R F M H A C I T R
T U U I I I L E G N A M S R M O
A E B Y L W K E A N R R F K A U
K O K B N U E C A A B F R M A G
R V W L A N C L I X O G U E R H
X A M I H D A Y B V U N A P U E
I P O H S I B D L O R A H I A N
M E T A M E L B O U R N E F L R
```

| | | | | |
|---|---|---|---|---|
| VICKI | CHARLENE | KATE LANDERS | KRISTIAN | GAIL | GUY |
| LAURA | MELBOURNE | COFFS HARBOUR | ROBINSON | LUCY | MAX |
| DANNY | RAMSAY | ERINSBOROUGH | FIONA CORKE | MIKE | JIM |
| MADGE | MRS MANGEL | HAROLD BISHOP | PAUL KEANE | JANE | TOM |
| HENRY | ROB LEWIS | EILEEN | NIKKI | ALAN | DES |
| SASHA | SCOTT | SHANE | FRED | | |

Answers on Page 61

# BEAUTIFUL AUSTRALIA

## Land of Contrasts

Australia is a land of dramatic contrasts. From the parched deserts of the interior, to the rolling beaches of the east coast, from the bustling activity of the big cities to the wide open spaces of the outback. Convicts sent to the penal colony in Botany Bay must have had mixed feelings about their new home, and some of their jailers were not altogether sure they wanted to be part of this new country, Australia. But other voices would disagree.

"I do not scruple to pronounce that in the whole world there is not a worse country. All that is contiguous to us is very barren and so forbidding that it may with truth be said that here nature is reversed; and if not so, she is nearly worn out."
**Robert Ross,
Lieut. Governor (1789)**

"It takes some time for the beauty of the open places to reach one's soul, but once there, hills, sea, river, wood, all are as nothing beside the beauty of the flat land that goes on and on in infinite space from sunrise to glorious sunset."
**Daisy Bates, writer (1938)**

"Let us drink a good health to our schemers above,
Who at length have contriv'd from this land to remove
Thieves, robbers and villains, they'll send 'em away,
To become a new people at Botany Bay.

The hulks and the jails had some thousands in store,
But out of the jails are ten thousand times more,
Who live by fraud, cheating, vile tricks and foul play,
And should all be sent over to Botany Bay."
**BOTANY BAY: A NEW SONG (1790)**

Photos by courtesy of the Australian Tourist Commission

# A SMART COOKIE

Stefan Dennis

**Stefan Dennis admits he was vile as a little boy, and takes a certain pride in being a bad but very likeable boy in Neighbours. One of the Neighbours originals, Stefan is still there and going strong.**

That ultra-chauvinistic pig of Ramsay Street, Paul Robinson, might have been called Pauline, if Stefan Dennis's early life had anything to do with it. Because of his shoulder length hair and ringlets as a youngster, Stefan started out in life as Stephanie because he looked like a girl!

Stefan, son of an English sea captain, gave his mother a hard time — so it didn't take them long to realize he was all male. "We were vile kids," recalls Stefan, "and Mum always thought of wild punishments for us. Mum may sound hard-hearted but she taught us right from wrong and I'm grateful."

Stefan enjoys being the Mr Nasty of **Neighbours**, but has ambitions to make it as a singer. Unfortunately **Neighbours** takes up most of his time. "We work hard. One of the problems working for a soap is that you're committed for weeks into the future, and it's hard to take up offers of other work."

Stefan has found time to make one single, however — *Don't It Make You Feel Good* — and had plans at one time to team up with Kylie Minogue. He and Kylie appeared in a charity concert in Melbourne. "Our one number was so popular the audience wanted an encore — so we did *Locomotion*. Afterwards I suggested we should get together singing-wise. But two weeks later a record company snapped her up."

Throughout the tough rise to fame Stefan has had the redoubtable support of his wife, Roz. Stefan and Roz have been married now for eleven years. Since the success of **Neighbours** they've been able to afford to move into a stylish house with acres of garden, where Stefan can indulge his passion for growing trees he specially imports from England.

## "We were vile kids"

Some of the show's success is because Stefan relates to the character of Paul, and the way that he developed the part after the loss of Paul's first wife, Terri. "Paul Robinson is a bit of a pig," he admits, "but he's a smart cookie. Paul lost faith in being a good guy, and decided to stay one step ahead."

One thing that does puzzle Stefan about Paul is what his on-screen character does with all his money. "He should have a huge amount of money," says Stefan. "I wish I'd been doing the things he's doing at 25 — but what on earth does he spend it on?"

Not that money is a worry to Stefan these days, with both he and Roz earning good livings. Roz is a top model in Australia.

"I love my wife very much," says Stefan, "but I want to stress something else — how much I love women in general, especially beautiful women."

Stefan feels very much at home in **Neighbours**, and he clearly enjoys his work. "The cast is generally very close," he says happily, "and I am particularly close to Fiona Corke." Like most of the older members of the cast, Stefan has worked hard to get where he is.

Now at last he can afford to relax a little and enjoy some of the fruits of his success. Now there's a lesson young Paul could do with learning from Stefan!

## "Paul lost faith in being a good guy"

# NEIGHBOURS GOSSIP

Craig McLachlan's first venture into feature films in an Aussie remake of the classic Casablanca has put him in the record books. Craig and co-star Dina Panozza (from Richmond Hill) clocked up a staggering 286 second non-stop kiss... beating the previous on-screen best of 185 seconds set by Jane Wyman and Regis Toomey in You're in the Army Now (1940).

With all the big screen debuts being made by a host of **Neighbours** stars it's worth recalling that Australia was there first. J. & N. Tait of Melbourne (home of **Neighbours**) made the very first feature film, The Story of the Kelly Gang, back in 1906 — six years before either the USA or Britain went into production.

The real thing! Six lucky teenagers won themselves the opportunity to visit Australia and meet the **Neighbours** stars on set. Winners of The Square Mile Project, sponsored by Essex Police and British Telecom, the girls won a trip to Australia and Hong Kong.

Team leader Julia Pinkney explained, "We visited a **Neighbours** exhibition as well as actually seeing the real things on our last day, when we met Henry, Mike and Des and various other characters. We also watched them filming and saw the sets of Lassiters and the Coffee Shop. It was a real experience."

No British soap opera, from Coronation Street to EastEnders has ever made it big in Australia.

Channel 4's series Citizen 2000, charting the lives of 20 children who will come of age in the year 2000, made a remarkable discovery. The children, who are now six years old, were all **Neighbours** experts — it was their favourite TV programme.

Guy Pearce is set for international film stardom at his first attempt. He stars in Heaven Tonight as Paul Dysart, an aspiring pop star. Movie producer Frank Howson says, "He is absolutely fantastic." Guy himself enjoyed the opportunity to develop a role. "I loved every minute of filming," he said. "It was so different after so much TV work. It's ironic that the first thing I do becomes an enormous success."

Thank heavens for the ad-free BBC! Australian viewers watching **Neighbours** on Channel 10 have to sit through not one, not two, but three helpings of adverts during **each** episode!

A light fingered thief made off with six weeks' scripts for **Neighbours** a few months back. It happened to one of the soap's scriptwriters whose Melbourne home was burgled while she was away on holiday. Fortunately they were copies and filming wasn't affected.

A detective commented, "The idea of someone stealing **Neighbours** scripts is something we would never have dreamed of." It was surely a coincidence that the same week Michael Parkinson spoiled thousands of people's breakfasts by spilling the soap's future secrets in his column, Parky Down Under in the Daily Mirror.

Anne Haddy's saddest memory of a fan letter was one from a young boy who asked her to paint a portrait of his dead cat. Helen Daniels was a keen, amateur painter, but, "I had to explain I wasn't a real artist," says Anne.

# NEIGHBOURS GOSSIP

Jessica Muscham

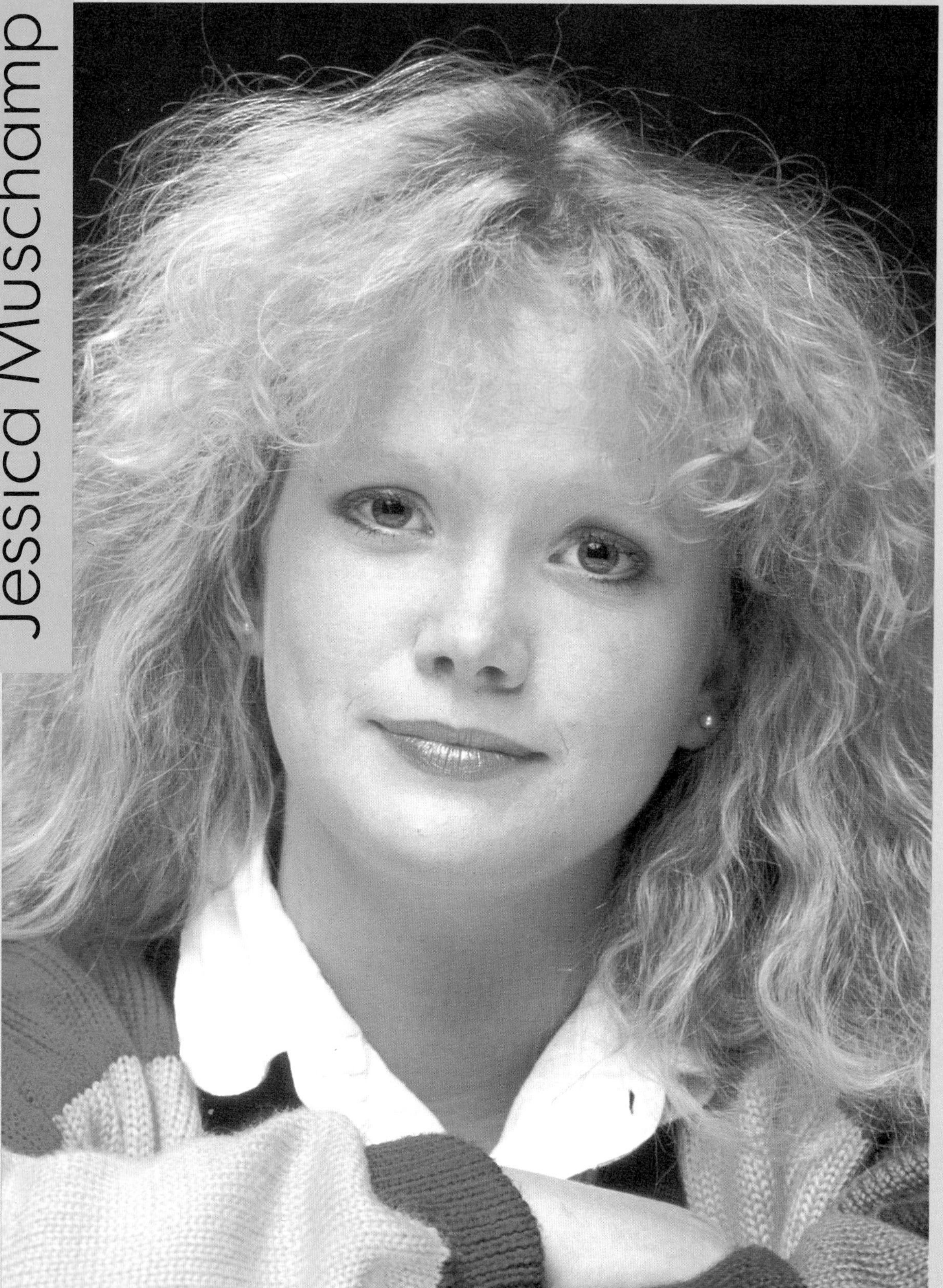

# BACK TO SCHOOL

## "I didn't expect to get the role"

**Neighbours** actress Jessica Muschamp believes working in the top-rating series actually helped her survive her gruelling final year of high school!

While most students would shudder at the thought of taking on a job during their all-important Higher School Certificate studies, Jessica felt the opposite.

And she was right! She passed her HSC with flying colours, earning 98 per cent for English, 87 for Literature, 78 for Australian History, 71 for French, and 67 for 18th Century History.

"I seriously think doing **Neighbours** is what got me through," the pretty 18-year-old explains. "I don't think I would have finished the year if I didn't have another thing to think about (other than HSC). At the beginning of the year I thought, 'I am not going into the school play, I will devote myself to school work'. When the **Neighbours** audition came up I thought it would be good experience — I didn't expect to get it (the role of Sharon Davies). When I did get it I had some serious thinking to do that weekend."

Jessica admits six months of dividing her time between portraying Sharon and studying hard wasn't easy. "It was very, very difficult having to go away from the Green Room (where the cast relax between scenes) to a little room by myself and study without a tutor," Jessica recalls.

"Sometimes the pace was very hard to handle. A few times I felt I couldn't go on any longer. Fortunately, that only happened a few times. I had so many people to support me — my teachers were pretty good as well as my family, friends and the kids at school."

While Jessica initially chose her subjects with the aim of doing a university arts or literary course, she nows wants to concentrate on acting.

"A lot of people said I should keep studying and get something behind me, but I will see what my career brings," explains the bubbly teenager, who was involved with school plays and sometimes created her own productions. "When I was about 10 I wrote plays and had the whole school coming to watch them!"

And although Jessica no longer has to worry about hitting the books between scenes, she will have to continue wearing a school uniform. Her character, Sharon, is still at school doing her Year 11 studies in the show. "It's like I have been sentenced to two more years of school," Jessica says, laughing.

## "Sometimes the pace was hard to handle"

Rachel Friend

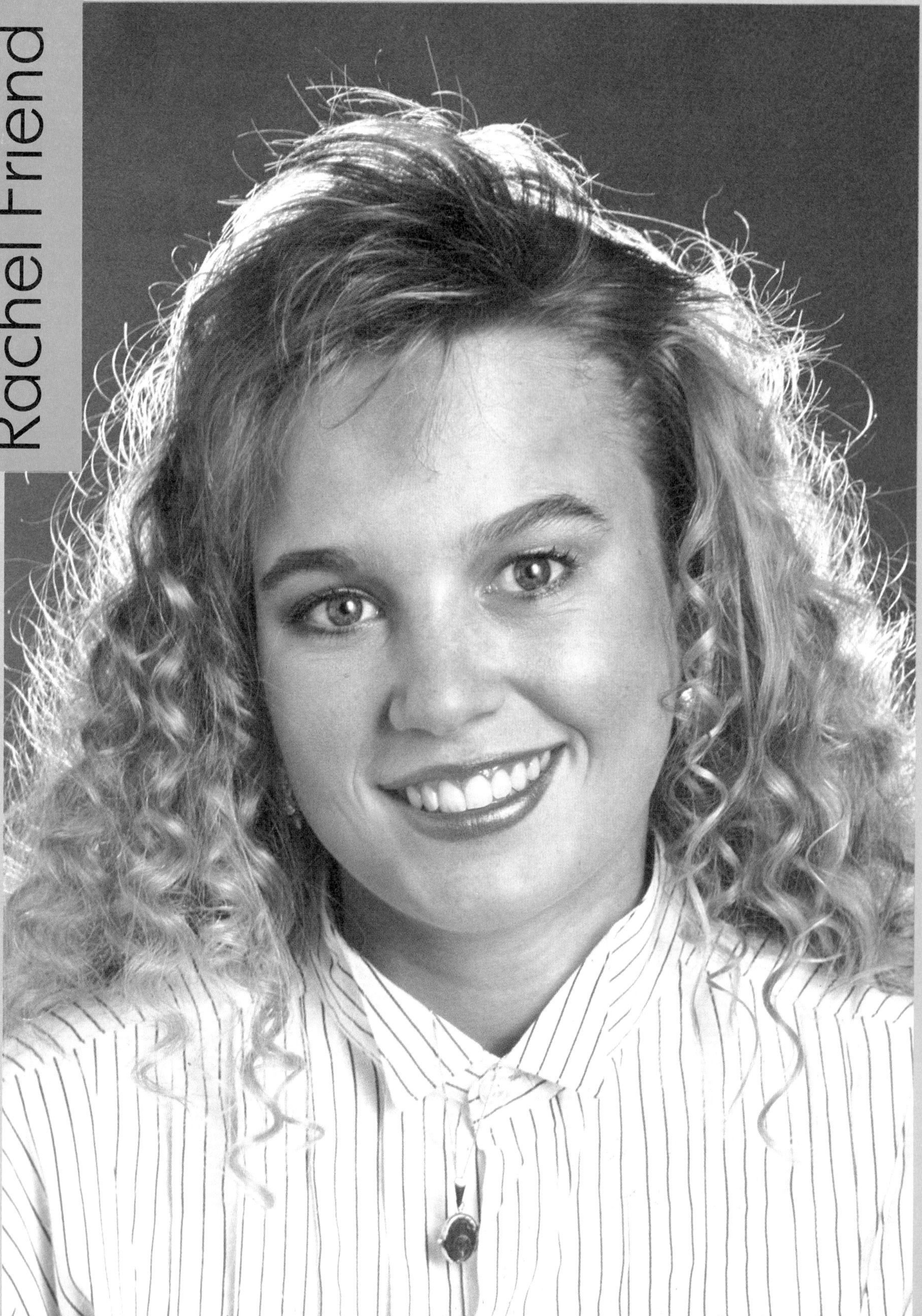

# QUIETLY CONFIDENT

**Neighbours** is gambling on a soapie newcomer to replace the volatile Charlene, now that Kylie Minogue is no longer with the show. Rachel Friend, who plays Bronwyn Davies, is a fresh face in the world of tv soaps, but she's determined to make her own distinctive contribution. The last thing she intends to be is a Kylie clone.

"I wouldn't really compare the characters because Bronwyn is a country girl and quite different from Charlene," Rachel says. It helps that Rachel counts herself as a **Neighbours** fan and has been a keen follower of the Ramsay Street saga during her own early days working in television, waiting for the break. Credits include a guest appearance on an axed soapie, *Prime Time*, and a part on ABC's *Home*.

Bronwyn arrives in Erinsborough and finds a hostel to stay in. At 18, after several years of helping to bring up her family after the death of her mother, Bronwyn has decided to head for the city. A course in child care makes her the perfect nanny for young Jamie Clark. Independent and not afraid to speak her mind, Bronwyn is practical and caring, with a definite tomboy streak.

Rachel shares certain things in common with her tv character, but says that they aren't very similar as people. "Bronwyn is not really outgoing but she is confident and I like that," says Rachel. "But I'm quieter than she is."

With the role of Bronwyn being Rachel's first big break into television she admits to being more than a little nervous about becoming a member of such a successful cast. "It is hard starting completely new, especially when everyone on the show is so well established," Rachel says, but fans in Australia seem to have taken her to heart, and British viewers will have their chance to see how Rachel shapes up very soon.

One of Rachel's main effects on the young, male inhabitants of Ramsay Street is to set their blood racing a little faster. Both Mike and Henry are set to have their hearts swayed by the new arrival. How did Rachel find shooting love scenes with the street's two most eligible young bachelors?

"When I was doing scenes with Guy it was new to me and I felt a bit funny," she says, "but now I'm a lot more comfortable." Craig, well-known for his on-set antics, clearly saw a chance too good to be missed. Laughs Rachel, "I can't say what he did after one scene, but it really left me red-faced!"

Craig, of course, is taking Henry's new on-screen romance in his stride. "I'm powering through the scenes without any bother. I do have a mean pucker and I feel like an athlete who has spent four years building up for the Olympics. Henry is going for gold!"

Whether Mike or Henry turns out to be the medal winner remains to be seen, but there's little doubt that Bronwyn is likely to break at least one heart on the way.

**"Bronwyn is quite different from Charlene"**

# LOVE THY
## *Neighbours*

## EPISODE THREE

*Henry is still keen to pursue his dog-orobics idea despite opposition from all sides. Meanwhile the brooch Mrs Mangel was saving for Jane has disappeared, and she has collapsed outside her house...*

The sudden downpour had stopped. In the quiet aftermath it was still possible to hear the ambulance siren as it faded away in the direction of Erinsborough Hospital. As Henry and Jane turned into Ramsay Street they could also see the cluster of people who were standing on the pavement.

"It's Nan!" said Jane anxiously. "I know it!" Some sixth sense told her instantly that it was her grandmother who had been taken ill. She broke away at once from Henry and began sprinting down the road.

Breathless, she and Henry came up to the small group of people gathered outside the house. Among them Jane made out, briefly, Beverly, Des, Mike. Her mind was a blur.

"Is it Nan? Is she all right?" she gasped.

Beverly came forward with a warm smile and put her arm round Jane's shoulder. "Your nan's all right, Jane. I merely called the ambulance as a precaution. She should have one or two tests to make sure there's nothing I've missed."

"Was it her heart? Did she – ?"

"No, it wasn't a heart attack, Jane, I'm very pleased to say," replied Beverly calmly and evenly. "She's a little dazed still. She fell and she's taken a nasty crack on the head, but I don't think it's serious."

"How soon will the ambulance be bringing her back?"

Beverly looked Jane directly in the eyes. "Tomorrow at the latest, I expect."

Jane was suddenly alarmed again and said, "Tomorrow? But why keep her in overnight if it's not serious?"

Beverly calmed her with a soothing look. "Simply a precaution. Routine observation. It's perfectly normal practice to be cautious with head injuries, especially over the first forty-eight hours. Relax, your nan's going to be fine. We just want to be one hundred per cent sure."

"I ought to go to the hospital," said Jane impulsively. There were tears in her eyes now. "If anything should happen to Nan – "

Beverly said calmly, "Give them a little time to run the tests and take the x-rays," said Beverly. "I'll go back now and see her myself.

I'll tell her to expect you at evening visiting."

"In the meantime," said Harold, appearing as if from nowhere, "what you need is a relaxing cup of camomile tea. It's just the thing! And you can come and eat with us. It's aduki bean casserole tonight," he added proudly, as if revealing a new wonder of the world, "one of my latest specialities."

"And if you survive that," quipped Des, joining them, "I'll run you up to the hospital later."

Jane looked at the circle of friendly faces. "Thanks everyone," she said, small tears beginning to well in her eyes again.

Madge came to stand beside Harold. "I'll come over and sleep at your house tonight, Jane. No arguments. I'll have supper ready when you get back from the hospital." Madge had taken charge.

She turned sharply on her heel and fixed Henry with a steely glaze. "As for you, Henry Ramsay, I want you in that house this minute! I have a few words I want to say to you."

"Here you are, Jane," said Harold in a kindly voice, handing her a cup of tea, "camomile, freshly brewed. Now you sit down here and drink it quietly." Harold ministered to his patient, while outside on the porch Des, Beverly and Madge discussed the situation.

"How is Nell, Beverly?" asked Madge, anxious to hear the news.

"All right superficially," said Beverly reservedly. "The cut on her head is nothing serious. What we have to wait to find out – and I haven't said anything to Jane so as not to alarm her unnecessarily – is whether it's simply concussion caused by the fall or . . . "

Beverly paused, not wanting to voice her thoughts, but she went on, "Or we may have to face the prospect there's something that happened that caused her to lose her balance in the first place."

"Like what?" asked Des.

"We can't say until we've seen the result of the tests, and kept Nell in for observation overnight," said Beverly. "I'm not prepared to guess at this stage."

"You mean it could be something serious

like a stroke, something like that?" said Madge quietly.

"Possibly," said Beverly. "Even if it is it may be not too serious. Nell was shocked and dazed, and not too sure where she was, but that could easily be simply the result of the blow as she fell. We must wait and see. Whatever you do, don't alarm Jane. If she needs to be told anything I'll tell when the time's right."

"Sure, Beverly, we won't breathe a word," Des assured her.

"There was one thing that puzzled me," said Beverly. "I couldn't make too much sense of it at the time. She kept muttering over and over about a brooch."

"That's easy enough," said Des. "She was at the bank this afternoon, arranging for it to be transferred to a safety deposit box."

Beverly drew in her breath thoughtfully. "She kept saying it was gone, it had been stolen. Do you think you could look into it, Des; it might put her mind at rest if we can tell her it's safe."

Des and Madge went inside as Beverly made her way back to her car to drive to the hospital. In the living room Harold was practising his bedside manner, calming Jane. Henry watched from the kitchen.

Des went and sat next to Jane on the other side from Harold. "Jane," Des began, "do you know anything about a brooch?"

"That!" said Jane. "We had a huge row about it last night. Nan said she'd been saving it to give to me when I got engaged. She was

worried that I was getting too friendly with Mike and Henry. She seemed to think I might end up marrying one of them, and that upset her. I told her not to be stupid: Mike and Henry are mates, that's all. She didn't like to think her precious piece of jewellery might end up in their hands. It was silly – a row over nothing."

"Did you see it? Do you know what became of it?"

"No, sorry. Is it important?" asked Jane.

Harold now spoke up. "Mrs Mangel was showing it to me yesterday when she was sitting on the settee."

"Did you see where she put it?" asked Madge.

"No," admitted Harold. "Wait a minute. I don't think she did put it away. We were in the middle of our discussion when she decided she had to go and look for Jane. Perhaps she forgot and left it lying around. I did warn her it wasn't safe."

"Come with me, Harold," said Des. "We'll go and have a look. Madge will look after Jane."

Ten minutes later they were back empty-handed.

"There's no sign of any burglary," said Des, "so I don't think anyone's broken in during the day. Did you see anything, Jane?"

"No, I just went home after work and sat down to watch a video Harold had lent Nan. Then Henry arrived, and we went out," explained Jane. "Nan must have come home not long after we'd gone. And I locked the door when I left."

"Something of a mystery," said Harold.

Later, while Des took Jane to visit her grandmother in hospital, Madge and Harold held a worried conference in their bedroom.

"I can't believe he'd do anything as stupid as that," said Harold.

"Nor can I," said Madge. "But it doesn't look good. As far as we know the brooch was lying out somewhere in Mrs Mangel's living room, and the only person to go into the house

"Would you like to have a dreadful daughter like Charlene?"

*Anne Charleston*

before Mrs Mangel arrived home was Henry. We know he was alone in the room while Jane went to fetch her coat. And now the brooch is missing. It can't be Henry can it, Harold? Tell me I'm imagining things."

"No, of course not," said Harold. "I know he's short of money for this scheme of his, but he wouldn't be that stupid, he couldn't be."

Madge and Harold gazed into each other's eyes looking for confirmation from the other that it was impossible.

"I could ask him outright, I suppose," said Harold. "Man to man, as it were."

"No, Harold," said Madge anxiously. "That would be as good as accusing him. We'll just have to hope Nell Mangel doesn't use that twisted logic of hers to set herself up as judge and jury. There's only one conclusion she'll come to. You know how she feels about Henry."

Harold tried not to show the worry in his face. He knew only too well what Mrs Mangel felt about 'criminal types' as she called them. "Let's hope we can clear all this up before Mrs Mangel gets back from hospital."

"Assuming she does come back," said Madge, her features tense and drawn.

It was the following day before firm news was available about Mrs Mangel's condition. Beverly knocked on the Ramsays' door and

was let in by Harold. Jane was sitting with Henry and Mike in the living room. Madge was in the kitchen fixing a snack.

"Jane," said Beverly going straight over to her.

"Nan? How is she?"

"Fine," said a relieved Beverly. "Just a mild concussion. She was in such a state when she found the brooch had gone she rushed out of the front door and slipped on the wet path. Nothing more serious than that. She's still got quite a headache, but that will pass. I've arranged for her to stay in until tomorrow. She'll be home by the afternoon."

Jane reached out and gave Beverly a big hug. Everyone burst into spontaneous gestures of relief at the news.

"That's great," said Henry. "Besides it means that you'll be able to take part tonight in the first, official, public demonstration of dogolympics, the revolutionary method of keeping your dog fit."

"Oh, Henry, no," said Madge despairingly.

Jane laughed. "Why not? I feel like running round the park a few times to blow the cobwebs out."

"Fantastic!" said Henry. "You in, Mike?"

"Sure, okay," said Mike.

Henry revealed his master plan. "I've arranged to borrow a couple of dozen dogs, and the owners are coming along to see the demonstration."

"A couple of dozen?" said Harold. "Isn't that a little ambitious?"

"No sweat," said Henry confidently. "Leave it to me. Mike and Jane can talk to the punters, I mean clients, about the dog-orobics routine – look, I've written it all out on these sheets for you. Where there's a space you fill in with some medical-scientific talk, you know the kind of thing."

Jane and Mike gulped. "No," they both said timorously.

"Oh, you'll think of something," said Henry with a big grin. "You've got a bit of time. The demo doesn't start for another couple of hours."

"A burnt-out old crocodile handbag."

Jean Rook in the *Daily Express*, describing Kylie Minogue

The park was busy. As well as two dozen owners and their two dozen dogs – everything from a great dane to a dachshund – Ramsay Street had turned out in force, in response to Henry's cajoling. Bouncer was the star pupil.

Henry called everyone together, and introduced his special consultants, although Mike and Jane seemed curiously reluctant to stand to the fore. Henry then instructed the owners to release their dogs, while he revealed a mysterious case which he proceeded to open. It was full of frisbees in all the colours of the rainbow, one for each dog.

The demonstration got no further. Bouncer, answering some primeval call, snatched the first frisbee from Henry's hand and set off at a tremendous pace across the park. Showing a singular lack of understanding of Henry's carefully planned schedule, the other two dozen dogs followed instantly in a mad, baying pack.

Henry stared in disbelief as Bouncer headed out of the park, closely pursued by a motley collection of varied hounds. This was definitely not part of the plan. He grinned weakly at the owners, trying to look as if he had everything under control.

The next instant he was roaring, "After them!" and an equally varied, if less athletic group of humans set out in pursuit.

Bouncer led them straight back to Mrs Mangel's house. He liked this game and he was particularly pleased that Henry had invited so many friends for him to play with. The frisbee didn't last long, after which, Bouncer thought that all his new pals might like to join him in a bit of a dig.

Henry, Mike and Jane arrived at the head of the human pack, just in time to stop the dogs digging up all of Mrs Mangel's carefully planted flowers and shrubs. Jane grabbed hold of Bouncer, who looked up delightedly and presented Jane with a small, velvet bag which he held in his mouth. It was rather grubby from where it had been buried in the garden, but inside was a perfectly intact brooch.

Mrs Mangel served the tea, handing cups to Jane, Mike and Henry.

"So you see, it must have been while Henry and I went to the park yesterday," explained Jane. "We left Bouncer behind. He must have found the bag where you left it, hidden it somewhere in the house, and then taken it out later and buried in the garden."

Mrs Mangel smiled. "And if it hadn't been for the three of you and your mad scheme we might never have found it. The idea may not have worked out, but I for one am very pleased that you thought it up in the first place. Without it . . . "

Henry smiled generously. "What are friends and neighbours for, Mrs Mangel?"

# BEAUTIFUL AUSTRALIA

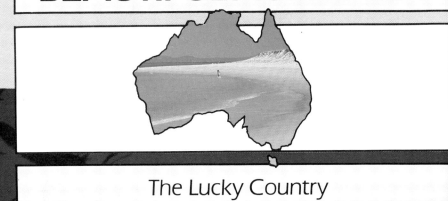

## The Lucky Country

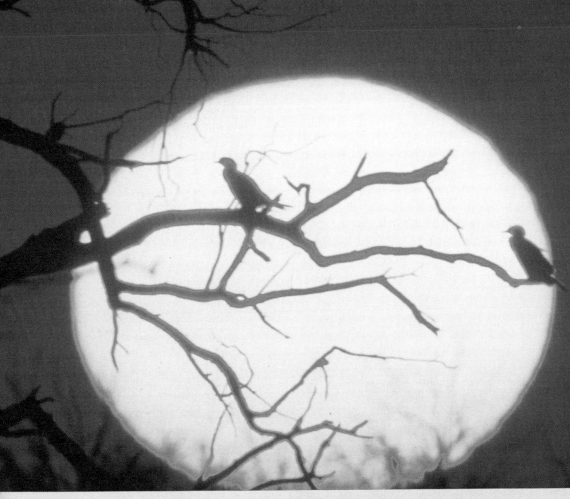

The Aborigines "may appear to some to be the most wretched people upon Earth, but in reality they are far happier than we Europeans; being wholly unacquainted not only with the superfluous but the necessary Conveniences so much sought after in Europe, they are happy in not knowing the use of them. They live in a Tranquillity which is not disturb'd by the Inequality of Condition; The Earth and sea of their own accord furnishes them with all things necessary for life... they live in a warm and fine Climate and enjoy a very wholesome Air, so that they have very little need of Clothing... In short they seem'd to set no Value upon anything we gave them, nor would they ever part with any thing of their own for any one article we could offer them; this in my opinion argues that they think of themselves provided with all the necessarys of Life."

*Captain Cook's first impressions, 1710*

Photos by courtesy of the Australian Tourist Commission

# NEIGHBOURS GOSSIP

Favours from **Neighbours**. Prompted by the ratings threat from the Aussie super-soap and *EastEnders*, ITV bosses fought back with the weekend omnibus version of *Coronation Street*. Actors from Granada's long running soap have good reason to thank their Aussie rivals. Repeat fees have doubled their wages overnight to nearly £2,000 a week — around five times the average rate of most of their **Neighbours** counterparts.

You have to be up early to catch Craig McLachlan's number one fan. The love-lorn lady leaves notes on the doorstep, which Craig's wife collects with the morning milk.

Anne Charleston thoroughly enjoyed her appearance as the Good Fairy in Oxford Apollo's *Jack and the Beanstalk* last Christmas. She rented an old farm during the two month run, and entertained visits from 16-year-old daughter, Emma, and 20-year-old son, Nick.

Like other **Neighbours** stars visiting the UK, Anne enthusiastically did numerous hospital visits and charity events. She felt very at home during her stay, but laughed, "No one warned me that it would be noisier here than Armadale, the suburb where we live in Melbourne — and the smell! Trust my luck to find a farm house which is surrounded by heaps of rotting manure!"

Hunky Heart-Throb Saves Soap SuperStar? Inspired perhaps by Indiana Jones' exploits, **Neighbours** stars Craig McLachlan and Annie Jones found themselves trapped on top of a roller coaster during filming recently.

While shooting scenes from the soap in Melbourne's Luna Park their carriage stopped because of an oil drip on the pulley that made the drive belt slip. The stars and crew got out and climbed the railings to the top. Then Craig helped staff and crew to push the carriage to safety. Admitted modest hero, Craig, "It was pretty hairy!"

Anne Haddy's film career includes appearing in Hostile Witness with Ray Milland. Vivean Gray appeared as the schoolteacher in the hit Australian movie Picnic at Hanging Rock.

The queue stretched in a long snake from the doors of the BBC shop to the security gates on Chichester Street and back again. Mums and toddlers, teenagers and senior citizens were all there. The place was Belfast's Cornmarket, the reason a visit by Stefan Dennis.

Indeed Stefan was a hit wherever he went during his UK visit earlier this year. And he took every opportunity to show what a good neighbour he is. In Aberdeen he made time to support the local HeadStart campaign, providing money to buy life-saving machines for use in Grampian, Orkney and Shetland. Said Stefan, "I'm happy to lend my support to such a good campaign."

New young stars Sally Jensen and Kristian Schmid had only one drama lesson before successfully auditioning for their parts as Kate and Todd Landers.

# NEIGHBOURS GOSSIP

Shaunna O'Grady

"The public aren't stupid"

# WILL THE REAL BEVERLY MARSHALL PLEASE STAND UP . . .

New **Neighbours** actress Shaunna O'Grady is following a precedent set by Jason Donovan — she's taken over the role of an established character.

Just as blond-haired Jason stepped into the shoes of dark-haired Darius Perkins in 1986 to play Scott Robinson, blonde Shaunna has replaced darker-haired Lisa Armytage as Dr Beverly Marshall.

"We don't look at all alike," says Shaunna. "Obviously we aren't the same person and there's been no attempt to make me look like Lisa. The public aren't stupid. It would be a mistake for me to try and pretend to be somebody I am not. I think I will just be recognized as a different actor and go on from there."

Lisa quit **Neighbours** in Australia in 1988, so the scriptwriters packed off her character to a medical conference in Perth for a couple of months. Beverly returned to the screen in March 1989, allowing Shaunna to make her **Neighbours** debut. British viewers will get their first look at Shaunna in the latter half of 1990.

Unfortunately Beverly's welcome home doesn't turn out to be as pleasant as she'd expected . . . "She found things weren't as she left them," Shaunna says, explaining how Beverly finds . . . but we won't spoil the story for viewers by giving it away.

Shaunna herself is a 33-year-old actress, and has been married to a theatre director for seven years, but during the past couple of years they have had to endure separations.

"Two and a half years ago we were living in Sydney when my husband got a job offer in Perth which was too good to refuse," recalls Shaunna. "So we packed up everything and left. We bought a fabulous house in Sydney just before we left. When we came back he had to go to Melbourne first. Then I was in the house three weeks when this job came up."

Shaunna is now living in Melbourne while she works on **Neighbours**, and she and her husband try to match up their schedules to spend as much time together as their busy careers allow.

"That sort of separation comes with the territory," says Shaunna. "It's just unfortunate it has happened quite a lot recently."

LISA ARMYTAGE

"Separation comes with the territory"

# The Ramsay Street Mastermind Quiz

1. What was the name of Lucy Robinson's pet egg?

2. Who claimed to have had Des Clarke's baby?

3. Name the child's real father.

4. Who conned Helen Daniels out of 50,000 dollars?

5. Who helped Helen regain the money?

6. Who brought a council inspector to visit the Coffee Shop?

7. What was the inspector's name?

8. What was the name of Vicki Gibbons' wheelbarrow?

9. Name Danny Ramsay's girlfriend.

10. What business was Clive Gibbons running when he moved into Ramsay Street?

11. Name the Senior Vice-President of Production of the Grundy organization.

12. Who was baby Sam's father?

13. Who was thought to have died of food poisoning?

14. Who prepared the supposedly poisoned food?

15. What kind of food was it?

16. How many times did Des Clarke fail to get married?

17. Name Clive Gibbons' girlfriend who died.

18. Of what did she die?

19. Name the actor who played the character of Max Ramsay.

20. Name Helen Daniels' adopted daughter.

21. What is the name of the local hotel?

22. What make was Clive Gibbons' car?

23. What was the name of Shane Ramsay's and Clive Gibbons' gardening business?

24. What did Des Clarke do the morning after his wedding?

25. Name Clive Gibbons' sister-in-law.

26. Name Mrs Mangel's grand-daughter.

27. Name Mrs York's dog.

28. What was Daphne's occupation before she moved to Ramsay Street?

29. What was the name of Max Ramsay's wife?

30. What was Graham Gibbons' hobby?

31. Who won the pancake-making contest at the Coffee Shop?

32. In which TV series did Kylie Minogue and Jason Donovan first work together?

33. Who was responsible for creating **Neighbours**?

34. Name the British soap on which he worked.

35. In which suburb of Melbourne is the real-life Ramsay Street located?

36. What is the street's real name?

37. Name the producer of **Neighbours** for Channel 7.

38. What was the name of Paul Robinson's first wife?

39. In which TV series does actor Peter O'Brien now appear?

40. What is actress Vivean Gray's favourite sport?

41. With whom did Lucy Robinson win a date?

42. Who actually kept the date?

43. Name the actor who originally portrayed Scott Robinson.

44. Name the member of the **Neighbours** cast who died suddenly in 1988.

45. Which character did she portray?

46. Can you name Craig McLachlan's favourite actress?

47. Which of the neighbours is portrayed by Ian Smith?

48. Where was Guy Pearce born?

49. Under which sign of the zodiac was Guy Pearce born?

50. How many cups of coffee a day does actor Stefan Dennis drink?

## NEIGHBOURS SEARCH-A-WORD

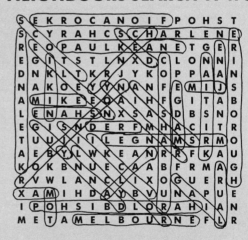

**SOLUTION**

**ANSWERS**

1. Eggward
2. Andrea
3. Gavin McKinley
4. Douglas Blake
5. Madge
6. Mrs Mangel
7. Mr Archibald
8. George
9. Marcie
10. An Animalgram Service
11. Peter Pinne
12. Fred Mitchell
13. Neddy the Cat
14. Eileen Clarke
15. Salmon Mousse
16. Four
17. Linda Lawry
18. A Cerebral Haemorrhage
19. Francis Bell
20. Rosemary
21. Lassiters
22. Honda Civic
23. R.A.G.S.
24. He slipped a disc
25. Kate
26. Jane
27. Billy
28. She was a stripper
29. Maria
30. Stamp collecting
31. Helen Daniels
32. Skyways
33. Reg Watson
34. Crossroads
35. Vermont
36. Pin-Oak Court
37. John Holmes
38. Terry
39. The Flying Doctors
40. Cricket
41. Rolf Pertwee
42. Nikki Dennison
43. Darius Perkins
44. Myra de Groot
45. Eileen Clarke
46. Minnie Mousel
47. Harold Bishop
48. Ely, in Cambridgeshire
49. Taurus
50. 20 to 30!

Photo by courtesy of the Australian Tourist Commission